The Wisdom of Sherlock Holmes

LITTLE ELM PRESS, LLC

This Journal Belongs to:

The past and the present are within my field of inquiry, but what a man may do in the future is a hard question to answer.

Some people without possessing genius have a remarkable power of stimulating it. I confess, my dear fellow, that I am very much in your debt.

There is nothing more stimulating than a case where everything goes against you.

_____

_____

_____

_____

_____

_____

_____

_____

_____

_____

_____

_____

_____

_____

_____

_____

_____

Crime is common. Logic is rare. Therefore it is upon the logic rather than upon the crime that you should dwell.

Under such circumstances I naturally gravitated to London, that great cesspool into which all the loungers and idlers of the Empire are irresistibly drained.

To a great mind, nothing is little,

What you do in this world is a matter of no consequence. The question is what can you make people believe you have done.

_____

_____

_____

_____

_____

_____

_____

_____

_____

_____

_____

_____

_____

_____

_____

_____

_____

_____

*A man always finds it hard to realize that he may have finally lost
a woman's love, however badly he may have treated her.*

_____

_____

_____

_____

_____

_____

_____

_____

_____

_____

_____

_____

_____

_____

_____

_____

_____

_____

_____

_____

I am a brain, Watson. The rest of me is a mere appendix.

There is nothing more deceptive than an obvious fact.

_____

_____

_____

_____

_____

_____

_____

_____

_____

_____

_____

_____

_____

_____

_____

_____

_____

_____

_____

_____

_____

There is nothing like first-hand evidence.

_____

How small we feel with our petty ambitions and strivings in the presence of the great elemental forces of Nature!

_____

_____

_____

_____

_____

_____

_____

_____

_____

_____

_____

_____

_____

_____

_____

_____

I never guess. It is a shocking habit,—destructive to the logical faculty.

_____

_____

_____

_____

_____

_____

_____

_____

_____

_____

_____

_____

_____

_____

_____

_____

_____

_____

"Data! Data! Data!" he cried impatiently. "I can't make bricks without clay."

What one man can invent another can discover.

_____

_____

_____

_____

_____

_____

_____

_____

_____

_____

_____

_____

_____

_____

_____

_____

_____

_____

There is nothing new under the sun. It has all been done before.

16

What object is served by this circle of misery and violence and fear? It must tend to some end, or else our universe is ruled by chance, which is unthinkable.

_____

My name is Sherlock Holmes. It is my business to know what other people do not know.

Strange enigma is man.

I cannot live without brain-work. What else is there to live for?

The world is full of obvious things which nobody by any chance ever observes.

_____

My mind is like a racing engine, tearing itself to pieces because it is not connected up with the work for which it was built.

Nothing clears up a case so much as stating it to another person.

You know my methods. Apply them!

 *A mind is an attic: keep yours well organized.*

The emotional qualities are atagonistic to clear reasoning.

It is a capital mistake to theorize before one has data. Insensibly one begins to twist facts to suit theories, instead of theories to suit facts.

_____

_____

_____

_____

_____

_____

_____

_____

_____

_____

_____

_____

_____

_____

_____

_____

_____

 *His face gets between me and my sleep.*

You see, but you do not observe. The distinction is clear.

It takes all sorts to make a world.

It is fortunate for this community that I am not a criminal.

When you have eliminated the impossible, whatever remains,
however improbable, must be the truth.

There is but one step from the grotesque to the horrible.

I presume nothing.

No man burdens his mind with small matters unless he has some very good reason for doing so.

_____

I never guess. It is a shocking habit,—destructive to the logical faculty.

It is better to learn wisdom late than never to learn it at all.

It's every man's business to see justice done.

38

A sandwich and a cup of coffee, and then off to violin-land, where all is sweetness and delicacy and harmony.

_____

_____

_____

_____

_____

_____

_____

_____

_____

_____

_____

_____

_____

_____

_____

_____

_____

_____

We have shared this same room for some years, and it would be amusing if we ended by sharing the same cell.

When a doctor does go wrong he is the first of criminals.

_____

_____

_____

_____

_____

_____

_____

_____

_____

_____

_____

_____

_____

_____

_____

_____

_____

_____

_____

_____

I have taken to living by my wits.

_____

One's ideas must be as broad as Nature if they are to interpret Nature

_____

Art in the blood is liable to take the strangest forms.

This looks like one of those unwelcome social summonses which call upon a man either to be bored or to lie.

_____

_____

_____

_____

_____

_____

_____

_____

_____

_____

_____

_____

_____

_____

_____

_____

_____

Watson, you can see everything. You fail, however, to reason from what you see.

A possession of all knowledge, which, even in these days of free education and encyclopaedias, is a somewhat rare accomplishment.

_____

_____

_____

_____

_____

_____

_____

_____

_____

_____

_____

_____

_____

_____

_____

_____

_____

I follow my own methods, and tell as much or as little as I choose.
That is the advantage of being unofficial.

My mind rebels at stagnation, give me problems, give me work.

_____

Education never ends, Watson. It is a series of lessons with the greatest for the last.

To Sherlock Holmes she is always the woman. I have seldom heard him mention her under any other name. In his eyes she eclipses and predominates the whole of her sex.

He is as brave as a bulldog and as tenacious as a lobster if he gets his claws upon anyone.

I am lost without my Boswell.

Come at once if convenient—if inconvenient come all the same.

TELEGRAM

I should prefer that you do not mention my name at all in connection with this case, as I choose to be only associated with those crimes which present some difficulty in their solution.

_____

Where there is no imagination, there is no horror.

Never trust to general impressions, my boy, but concentrate yourself upon details.

Violence does, in truth, recoil upon the violent, and the schemer falls into the pit which he digs for another.

_____

_____

_____

_____

_____

_____

_____

_____

_____

_____

_____

_____

_____

_____

_____

_____

_____

_____

_____

It's a wicked world, and when a clever man turns his brain to crime it is the worst of all.

You have the grand gift of silence, Watson; it makes you quite invaluable as a companion.

_____

_____

_____

_____

_____

_____

_____

_____

_____

_____

_____

_____

_____

_____

_____

_____

_____

_____

_____

_____

It is stupidity rather than courage to refuse to recognize danger when it is close upon you.

We reach. We grasp. And what is left in our hands at the end? A shadow. Or worse than a shadow—misery.

_____

_____

_____

_____

_____

_____

_____

_____

_____

_____

_____

_____

_____

_____

_____

_____

My life is spent in one long effort to escape from the commonplaces of existence. These little problems help me to do so.

_____

_____

_____

_____

_____

_____

_____

_____

_____

_____

_____

_____

_____

_____

_____

_____

_____

He sits motionless, like a spider in the center of its web, but that web has a thousand radiations, and he knows well every quiver of each of them.

It is a mistake to confound strangeness with mystery. I abhor the dull routine of existence.

_____

I cannot agree with those who rank modesty among the virtues. To the logician all things should be seen exactly as they are, and to underestimate one's self is as much a departure from truth as to exaggerate one's own powers.

A trusty comrade is always of use; and a chronicler still more so.

It has long been an axiom of mine that the little things are infinitely the most important.

 *I think that there are certain crimes which the law cannot touch, and which therefore, to some extent, justify private revenge.*

_____

_____
_____
_____
_____
_____
_____
_____
_____
_____
_____
_____
_____
_____
_____
_____
_____
_____
_____

Circumstantial evidence is a very tricky thing. It may seem to point very straight to one thing, but if you shift your own point of view a little, you may find it pointing in an equally uncompromising manner to something entirely different.

Work is the best antidote of sorrow, my dear Watson.

The game is afoot.

The fair sex is your department.

The lowest and vilest alleys in London do not present a more dreadful record of sin than does the smiling and beautiful countryside.

Man, or at least criminal man, has lost all enterprise and originality. As to my own little practice, it seems to be degenerating into an agency for recovering lost lead pencils and giving advice to young ladies from boarding schools.

I know, my dear Watson, that you share my love of all that is bizarre and outside the conventions and humdrum routine of daily life.

I am somewhat exhausted; I wonder how a battery feels when it pours electricity into a non-conductor.

_____

_____

_____

_____

_____

_____

_____

_____

_____

_____

_____

_____

_____

_____

_____

_____

Never have I seen a man run as Holmes ran that night.

I am not the law, but I represent justice so far as my feeble powers go.

_____

You know a conjurer gets no credit when once he has explained his trick.

While the individual man is an insoluble puzzle, in the aggregate he becomes a mathematical certainty.

I listen to their story, they listen to my comments, and then I pocket my fee.

Having gathered these facts, Watson, I smoked several pipes over them, trying to separate those which were crucial from others which were merely incidental.

I never remember feeling tired by work, though idleness exhausts me completely.

It is only goodness which gives extras, and so I say again that we have much to hope from the flowers.

They say that genius is an infinite capacity for taking pains.
It's a very bad definition, but it does apply to detective work.

Holmes took his revolver from his drawer and slipped it in his pocket. It was clear that he thought that our night's work might be a serious one.

I must thank you for calling my attention to a case which certainly presents some features of interest. I had observed some newspaper comment at the time, but I was exceedingly preoccupied by that little affair of the Vatican cameos, and in my anxiety to oblige the Pope, I lost touch with several interesting English cases.

Holmes loved to lie in the very centre of five million of people, with his filaments stretching out and running through them, responsive to every little rumor or suspicion of unsolved crime.

My horror at his crimes was lost in my admiration at his skill.

If we could fly out of that window hand in hand, hover over this great city, gently remove the roofs, and and peep in at the queer things which are going on, the strange coincidences, the plannings, the cross-purposes, the wonderful chains of events, working through generations, and leading to the most outre results, it would make all fiction with its conventionalities and foreseen conclusions most stale and unprofitable.

There are fifty who can reason synthetically for one who can reason analytically.

*Now is the dramatic moment of fate, Watson. When you hear a
step upon the stair which is walking into your life, and you
know not whether for good or ill.*

Good heavens, Watson, what has become of any brains that God has given me?

It is not my intention to be fulsome, but I confess that I covet your skull.

I must apologize for calling so late and I must further beg you to be so unconventional as to allow me to leave your house presently by scrambling over your back garden wall.

The best way of successfully acting a part is to be it.